Samson and Delilah

© 1997 Grandreams Limited

Published by
Grandreams Limited
435-437 Edgware Road
Little Venice
London W2 1TH

Printed in Hong Kong

A long time ago in the land of Canaan, there lived an Israelite man called Samson. He was the strongest man who ever lived, and could score a lion with one look. God had given Samson this strength because he planned for him to save Israel from the Philistines, who were very bad people.

Samson often visited the Philistine soldiers in Tinmath and bated them, for he knew no man could ever hurt him. The power of his strength was a secret that even his parents did not know of. The Philistines were terrified of Samson. They decided that something must be done to take away his power and enslave him.

One day while visiting Tinmath, Samson set eyes on the most beautiful girl he had ever seen. Her name was Delilah, and she was a Philistine, but this did not worry Samson. He bent down on one knee, and told Delilah of his feelings.

The Philistines soon got word of the love between Samson and Delilah, and they promised 1,100 pieces of silver to Delilah if she would share the secret of Samson's strength. Delilah was a Philistine after all, and was therefore very bad. Her love for Samson was not true, and in her greed she accepted the offer made to her.

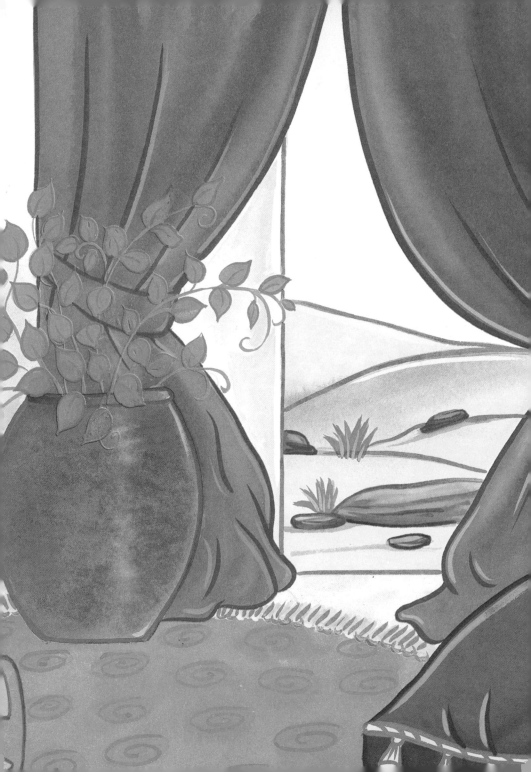

Delilah begged Samson to tell her his secret but he refused, until she wept. Samson felt guilty, and so he told her, "Delilah, the power of my strength is in my locks of hair. Shave me and I am a helpless kitten."

Delilah then waited until Samson fell asleep, and called a man in to cut off Samson's locks of hair. Delilah was paid her 1,100 pieces of silver and in her greed, before fleeing, she counted every penny to make sure it was all there.

When Samson awoke he was surrounded by Philistine soldiers. He tried to fight the men, but they held him down and bound his hands.

"So the strong lion has become a weak kitten," laughed one soldier. "Your hair has gone Samson, you are a prisoner now!"

The Philistines put out Samson's eyes and threw him into a prison cell, for months. But the Philistines did not realize that Samson's hair was growing back, and, of course, with the hair came back the strength.

One day the Philistines had a big party at the palace and Samson was brought out of prison to be mocked for entertainment. He was put in between two pillars, and the crowds laughed and jeered at him, "Samson the kitten, Samson the kitten."

But Samson was no longer a kitten. His hair had grown back and he was again the strongest man in the world. With all his power he pushed against the huge pillars, bringing the kingdom around him crashing down, and destroying the Philistines forever.